Mrs Wordsmith.

See It!
Stick It!
Sight Words

Volume 2

Made with ♥ by word warriors
in London and Los Angeles.

mrswordsmith.com

Get to know your Sight Words Sticker Book

Introduction

This book will help children learn 100 of the highest-frequency English words (see *See It! Stick It! Volume 1* for another 100 words). To become strong readers, children need to be able to notice and read these words instantly. *See It! Stick It!* is an interactive book that makes it easy to master these critical words.

What are sight words?

Sight words are high-frequency words that often involve irregular spelling, making them tricky to decode. Because they are so frequent, stumbling across these words can slow down children's reading significantly. This is why literacy experts recommend that children learn by heart what these words look like. Automatically reading these words in texts leaves children's brains free to decode less frequent words with more regular spelling; reading becomes more fluent and they can focus on comprehending the meaning of what they are reading. Our sight words selection is based on the most widely used lists of sight words.

Meet the Scooties

Grit

Shang High

Armie

Bearnice

Bogart

Oz

Brick

Yin & Yang

Plato

Instructions for parents

1. Can your child read the word? Help them if they don't know it. Together, read the example sentence to clarify the meaning of the word and provide a context for it. Then ask your child to read the main word again. If they get stuck, encourage them!

2. Flip to the sticker pages at the back of the book and look for the sticker that matches the word. When you find it, have your child say the word again.

   Tip: flipping to the back page is good for practice, because your child has to hold the word in their working memory to look for it again on the sticker page.

3. Peel off the sticker and flip back to the word page. Have your child place the sticker on the correct word, and read the word again.

4. If your child trips up, help them get it right next time: move your finger underneath the word from left to right and read it aloud. Then ask your child to say it while you move your finger underneath the word. This reinforces the connection between what the word looks like and what it sounds like.

5. Once the stickers are in place, you can browse the book with your child until they become fluent in reading these words.

Get sticking!

Sticker page

4

Sight word

Example sentence

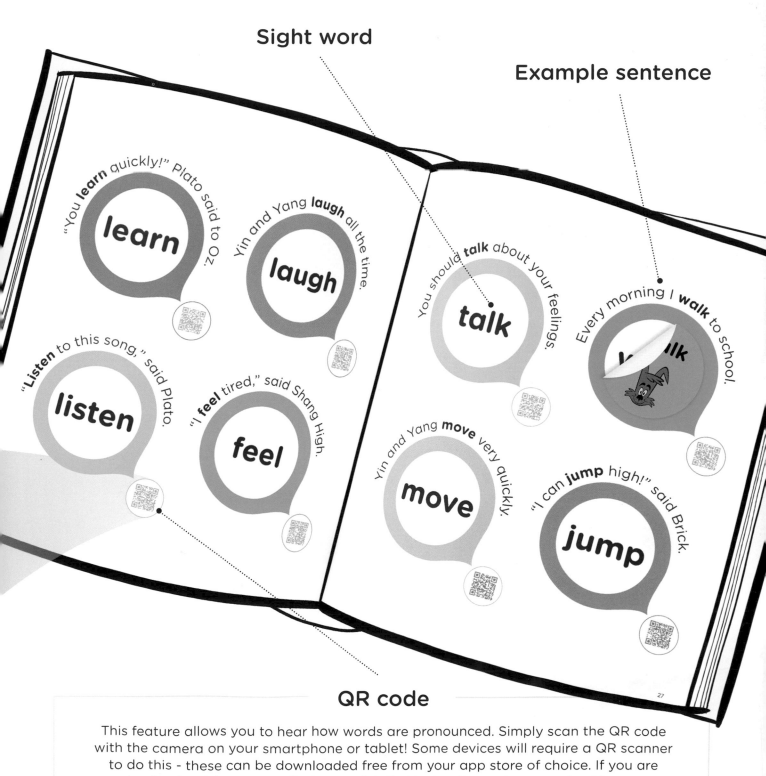

"You **learn** quickly!" Plato said to Oz.

learn

Yin and Yang **laugh** all the time.

laugh

"**Listen** to this song," said Plato.

listen

"I **feel** tired," said Shang High.

feel

You should **talk** about your feelings.

talk

Every morning I **walk** to school.

walk

Yin and Yang **move** very quickly.

move

"I can **jump** high!" said Brick.

jump

27

QR code

This feature allows you to hear how words are pronounced. Simply scan the QR code with the camera on your smartphone or tablet! Some devices will require a QR scanner to do this - these can be downloaded free from your app store of choice. If you are having trouble, you can find more detailed instructions at mrswordsmith.com

Grit has **one** tail.

one

Shang High has **two** eyes.

two

My tricycle has **three** wheels.

three

Yang has **four** legs.

four

7

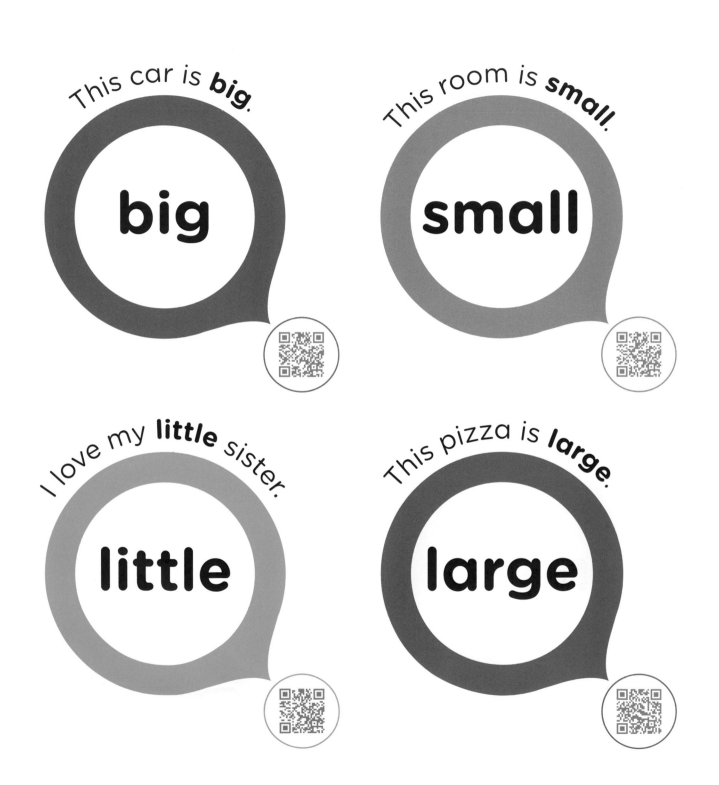

This car is **big**.

big

This room is **small**.

small

I love my **little** sister.

little

This pizza is **large**.

large

My **first** bike was red.

first

I had the **last** piece of cake.

last

You **only** have one chance.

only

There is **enough** cake for everyone.

enough

11

This is **my** scooter.

my

Where is **your** coat?

your

This is **our** house.

our

That is **their** dog.

their

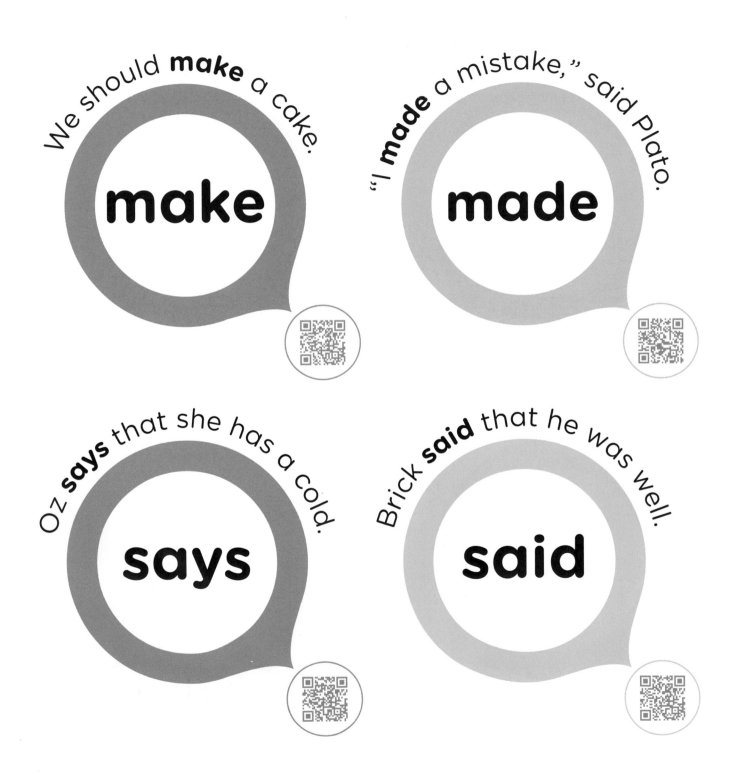

We should **make** a cake.

make

"I **made** a mistake," said Plato.

made

Oz **says** that she has a cold.

says

Brick **said** that he was well.

said

14

"**Take** care!" said Bogart.

take

Plato **took** off his hat.

took

Can you **bring** me some water?

bring

Brick said he would **carry** the bags.

carry

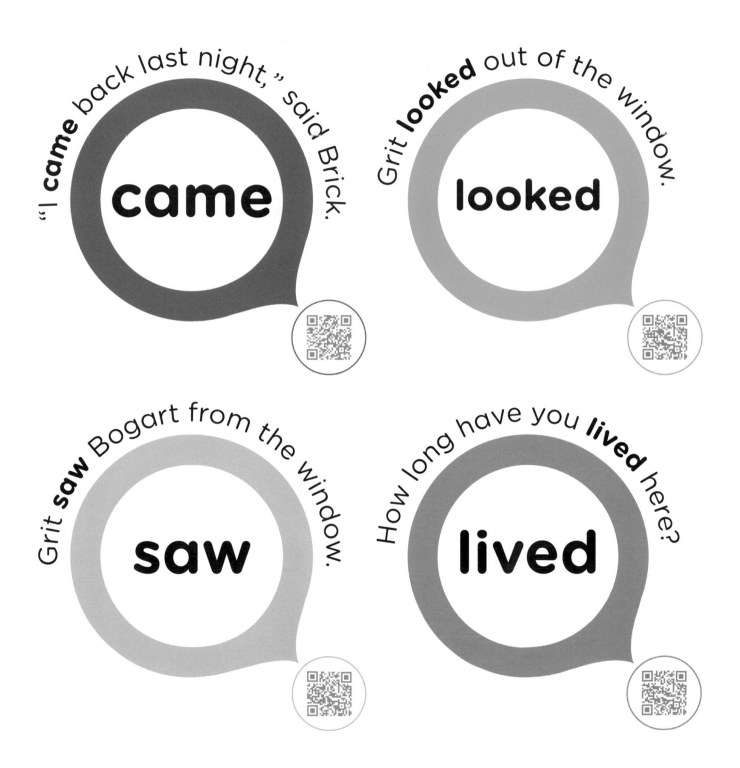

"I **came** back last night," said Brick.

came

Grit **looked** out of the window.

looked

Grit **saw** Bogart from the window.

saw

How long have you **lived** here?

lived

Can I **ask** you something?

ask

Armie **asked** what time it was.

asked

"I will **call** you later," said Oz.

call

They **called** a doctor.

called

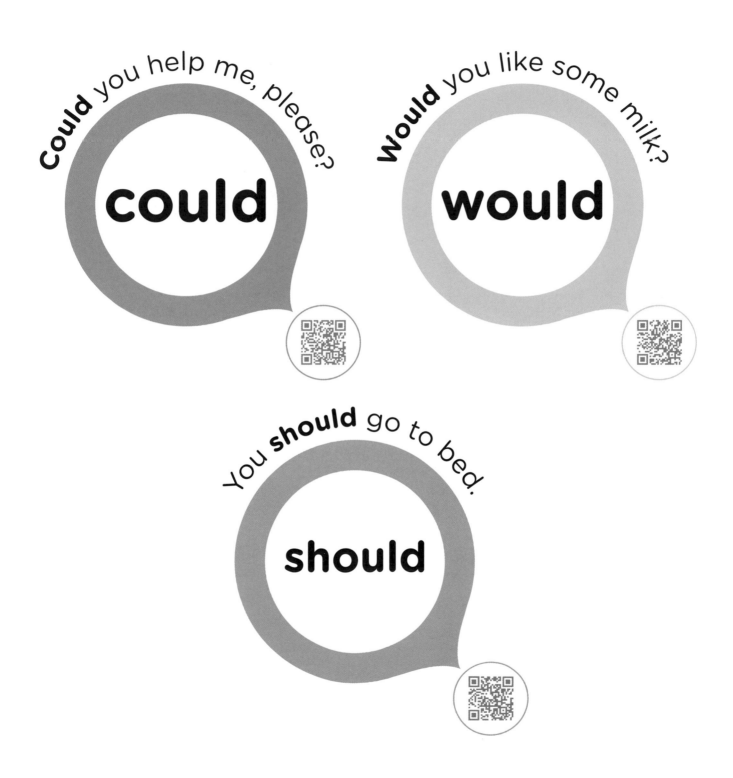

"I **may** go to the party," said Plato.

may

"You **must** try this cake," said Yin.

must

"I **might** be late," said Shang High.

might

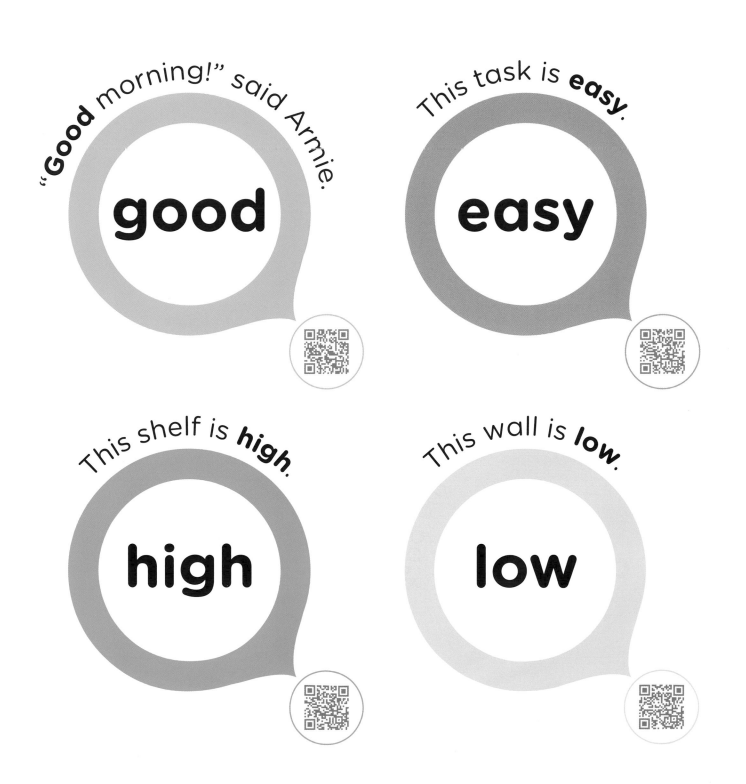

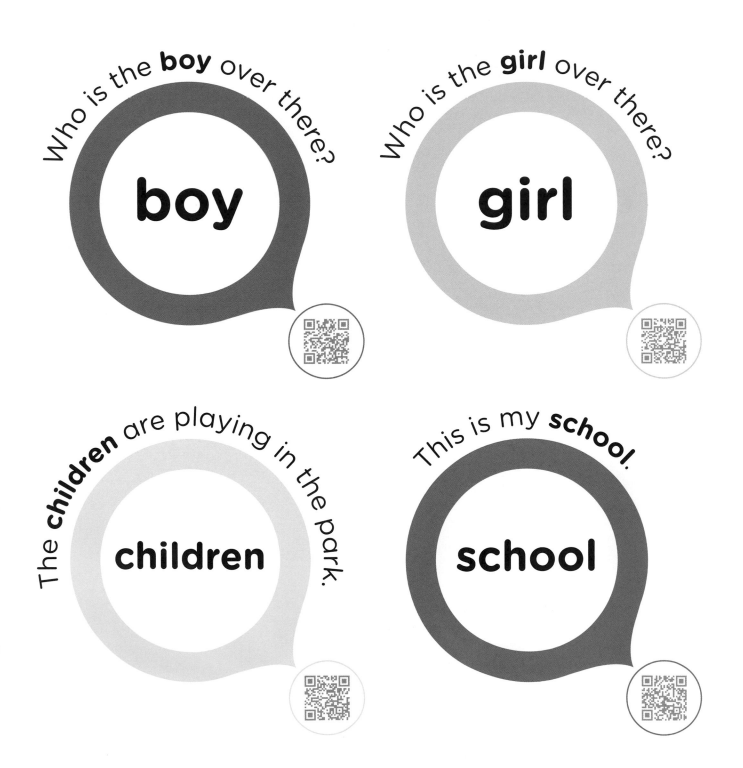

Who is the **boy** over there?

boy

Who is the **girl** over there?

girl

The **children** are playing in the park.

children

This is my **school**.

school

22

My **mother** is funny.

mother

My **father** is kind.

father

My **brother** is smart.

brother

You are my best **friend**.

friend

23

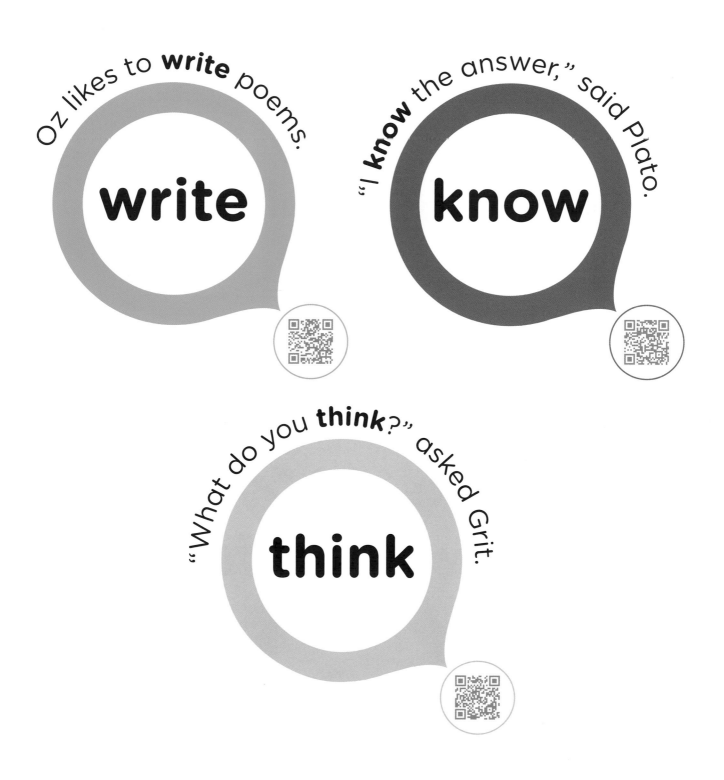

You should **talk** about your feelings.

talk

Every morning I **walk** to school.

walk

Yin and Yang **move** very quickly.

move

"I can **jump** high!" said Brick.

jump

27

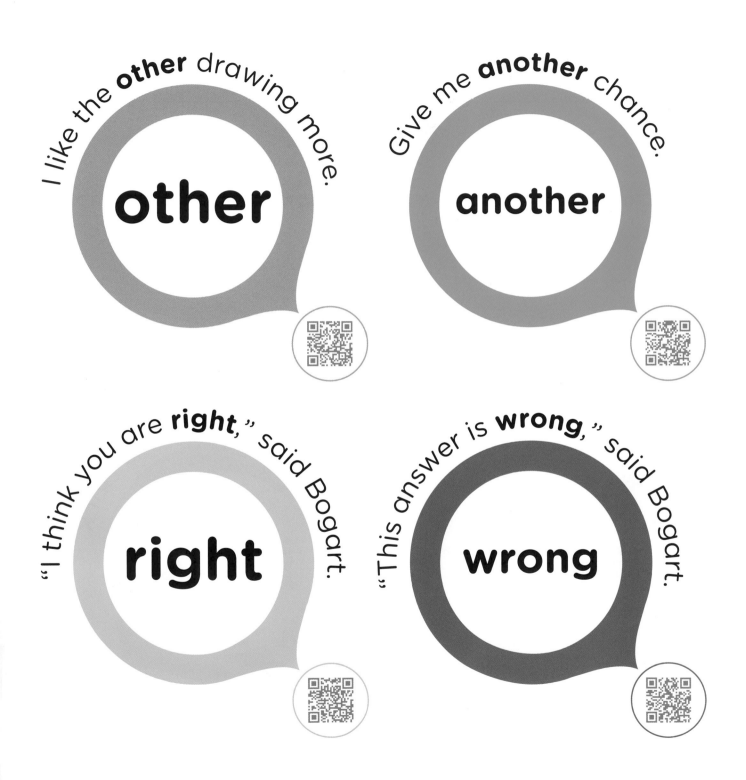

28

"I need to go **now**," said Grit.

now

You should **never** be mean.

never

Armie wakes up **early**.

early

"**Today** is my birthday," said Bearnice.

today

I went to the zoo **once**.

once

Plato reads **often**.

often

Oz **usually** goes to bed early.

usually

I **always** wash my hands before lunch.

always

"Do not do this **again**," said Grit.

again

"I will think **about** it," said Armie.

about

Brick is happy **because** it is his birthday.

because

"Spring is **finally** here," said Oz.

finally

about, p31
about

again, p31
again

also, p13
also

always, p30
always

another, p28
another

aren't, p11
aren't

ask, p18
ask

asked, p18
asked

because, p31
because

big, p8
big

boy, p22
boy

bring, p16
bring

brother

buy

call

called

came

carry

children

come

could

early

easy

enough

father

feel

few

finally

find

first

four

friend

girl

give

go

going

good

high

house

I'm

isn't

it's

jump

know

large

last

laugh

learn

listen, p26

little, p8

lived, p17

looked, p17

low, p21

made, p14

make, p14

may, p20

might, p20

mother, p23

move, p27

must, p20

my

never

new

now

often

old

once

one

only

other

our

right

road, p24 **road**

said, p14 **said**

same, p13 **same**

saw, p17 **saw**

says, p14 **says**

school, p22 **school**

sea, p24 **sea**

should, p19 **should**

small, p8 **small**

so, p13 **so**

some, p7 **some**

take, p16 **take**

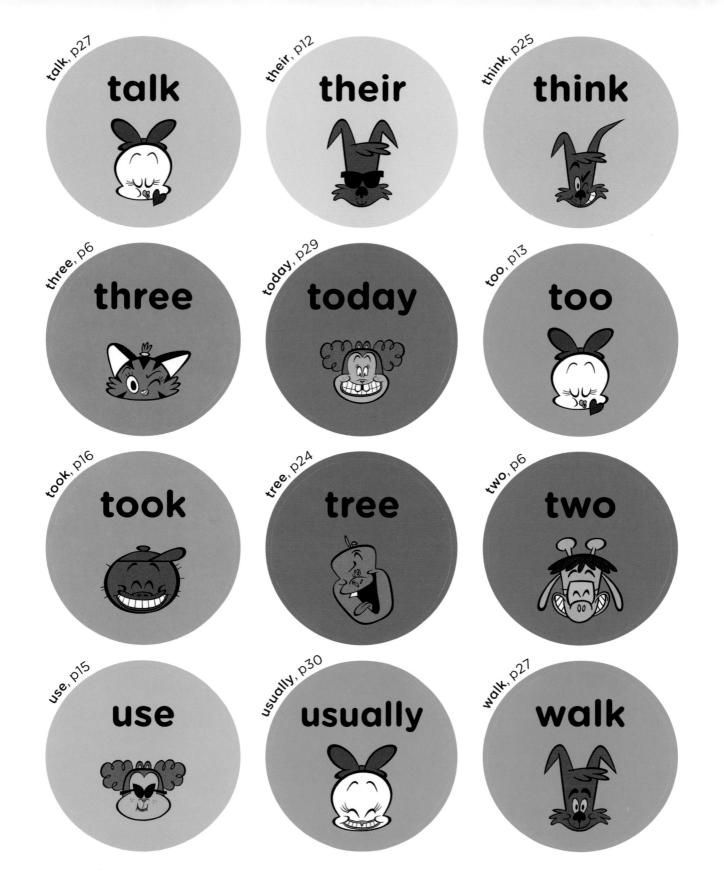

went, p10

would, p19

write, p25

wrong, p28

your, p12